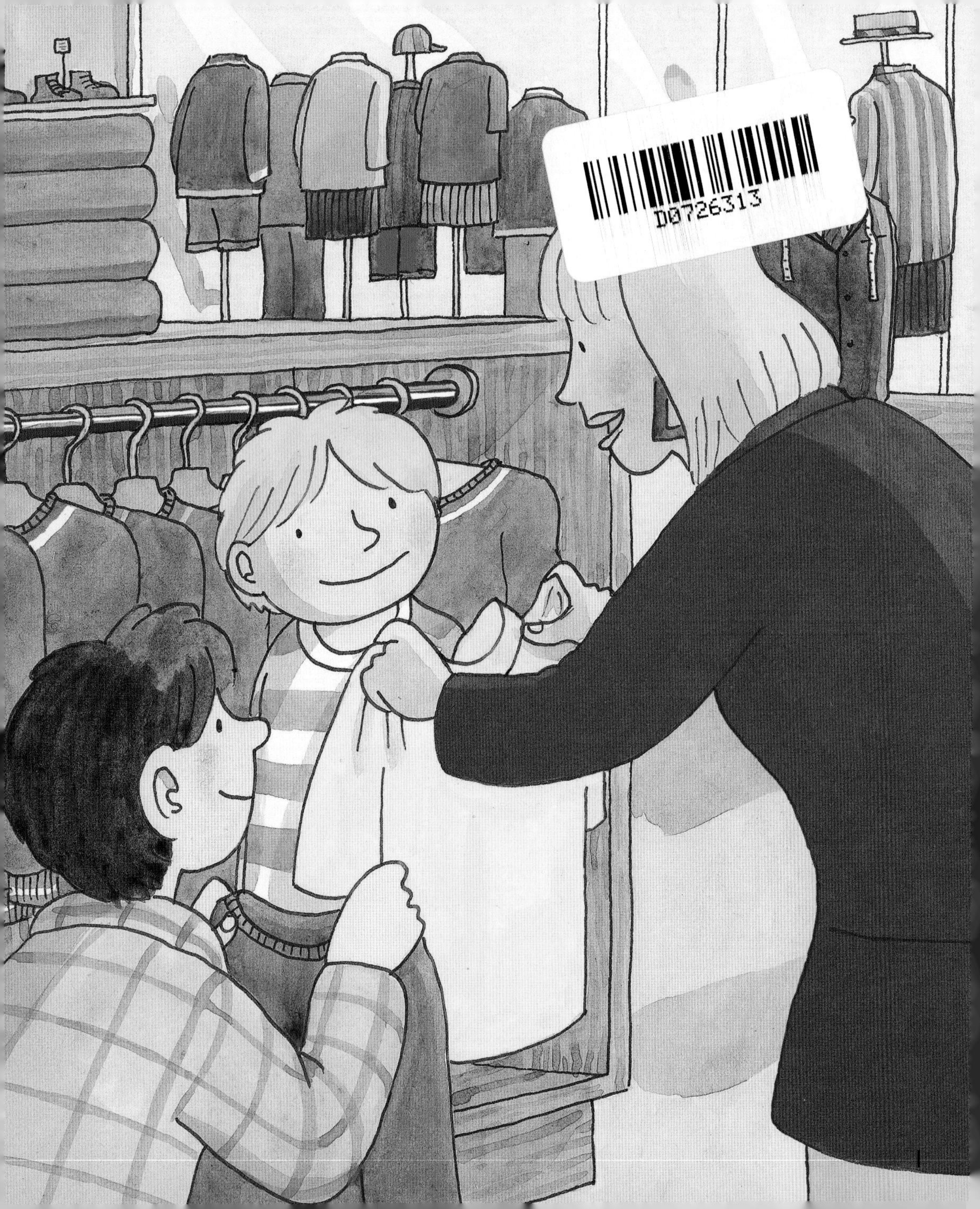

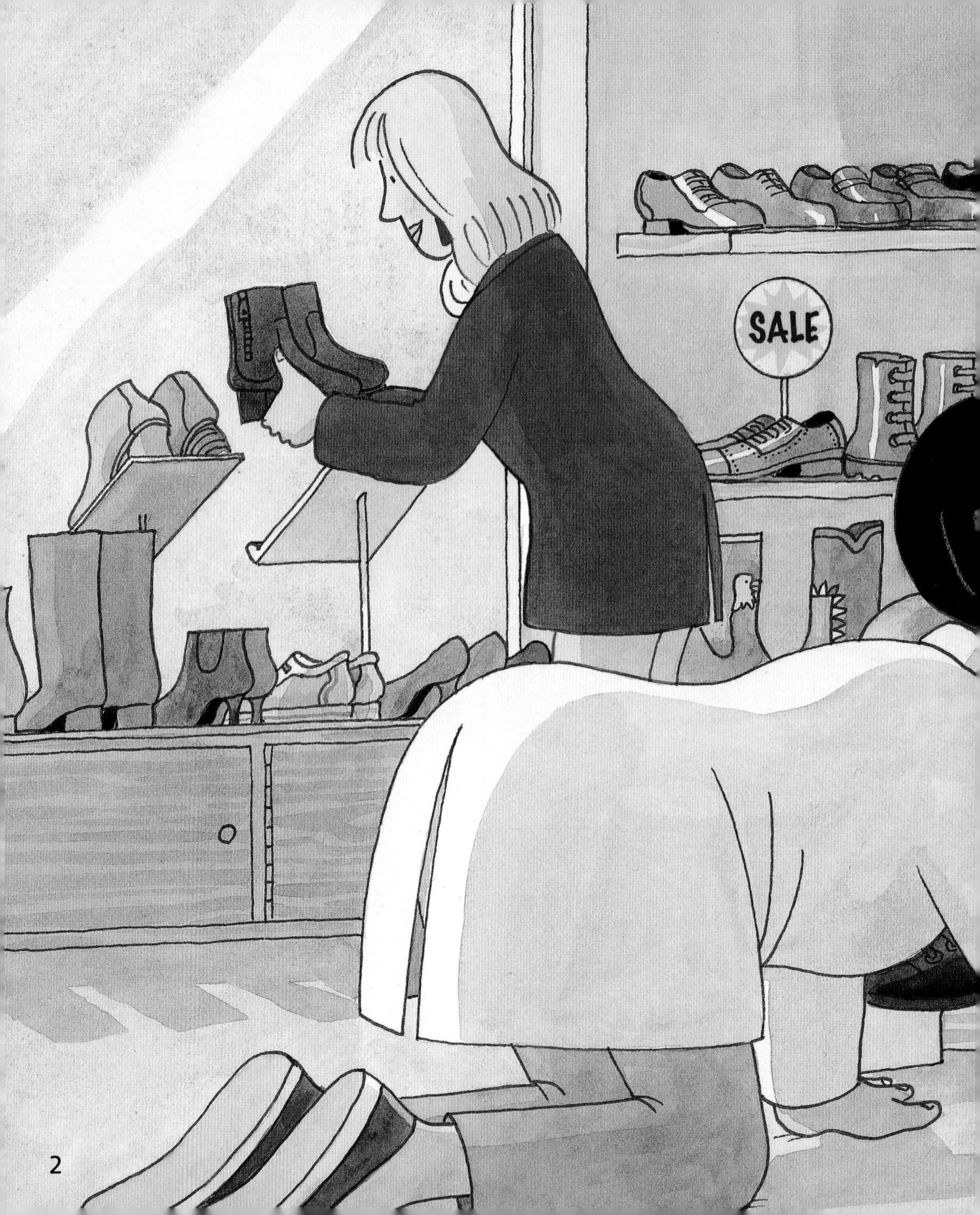
SALE

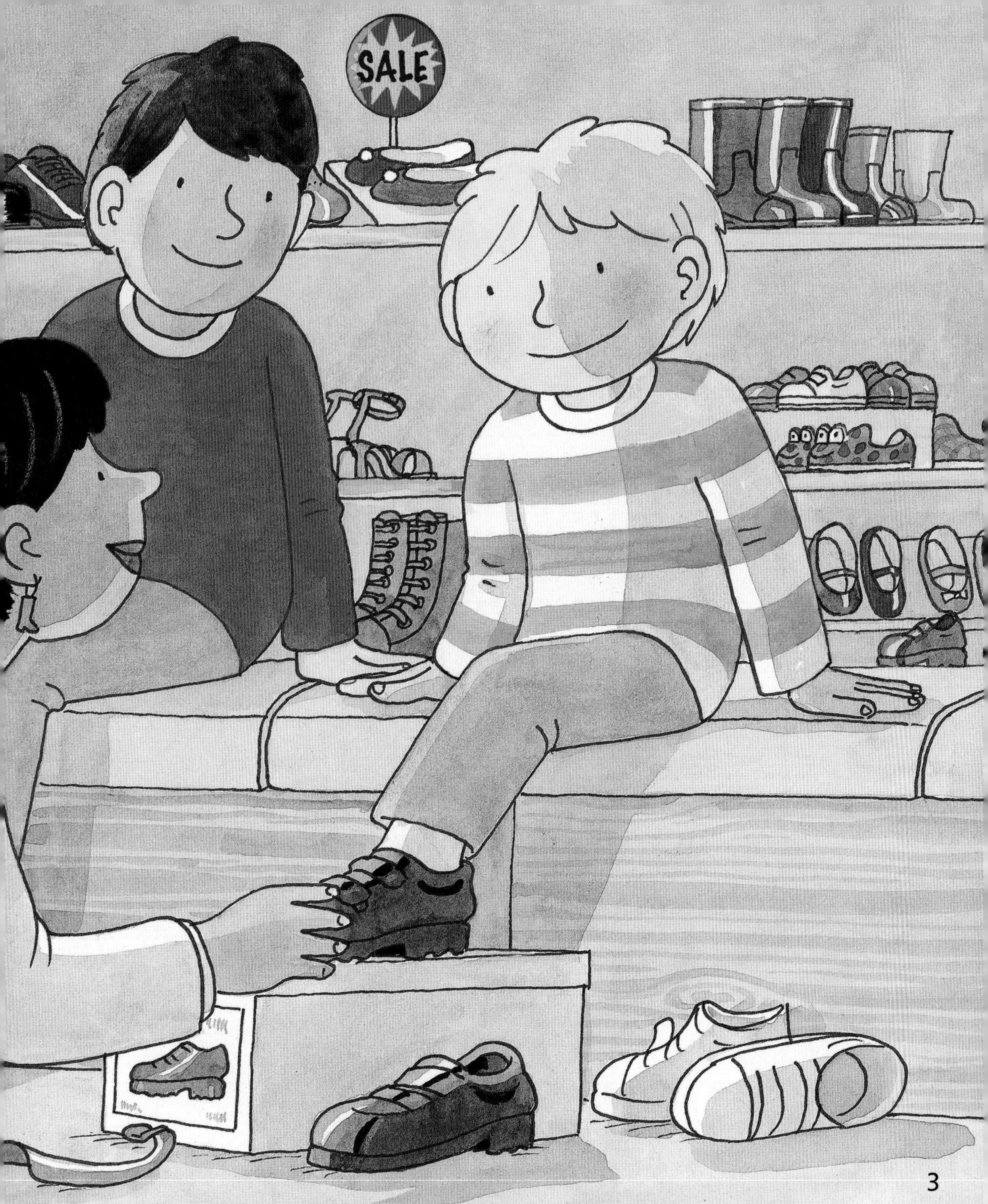
SALE

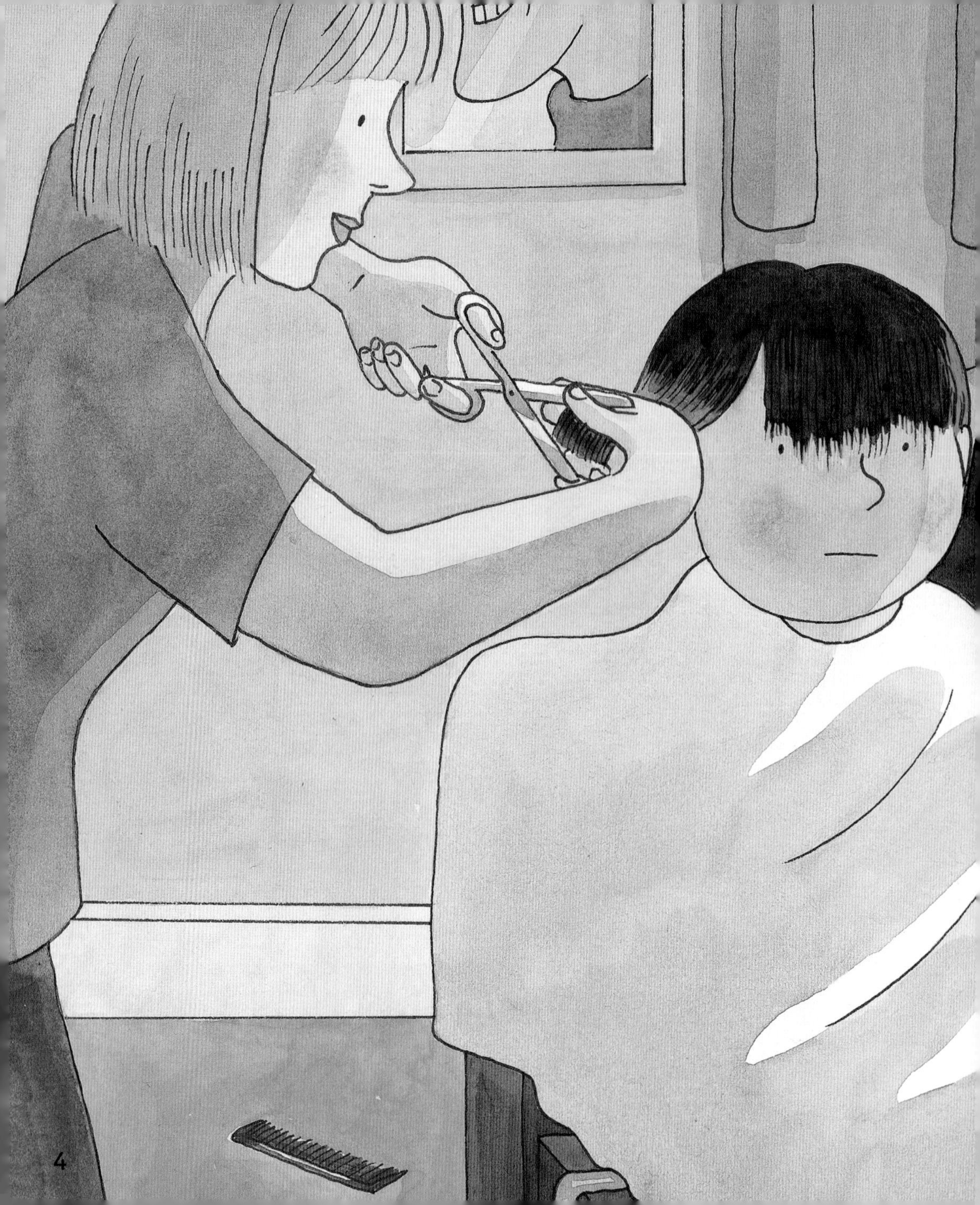

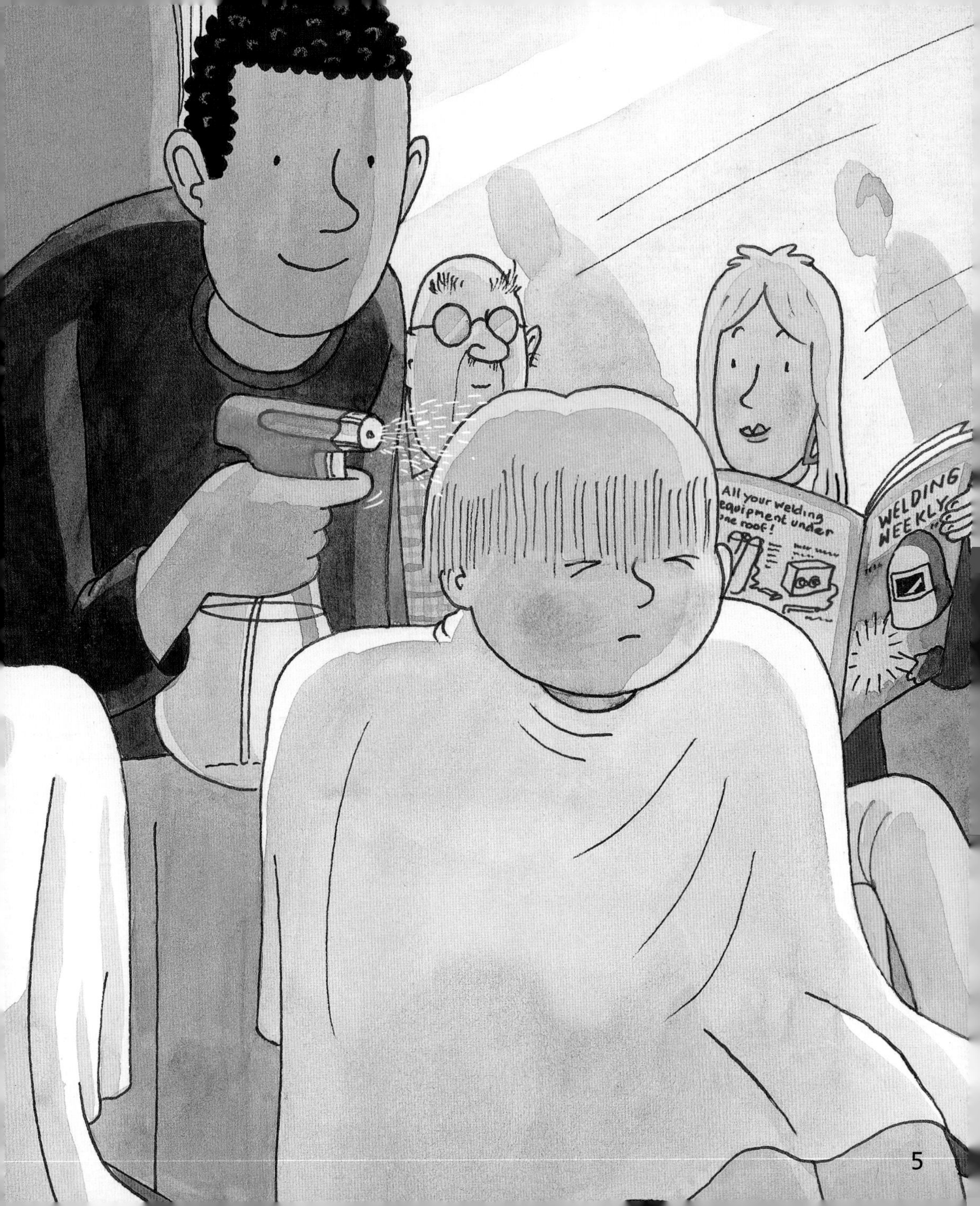
All your welding equipment under one roof!
WELDING WEEKLY

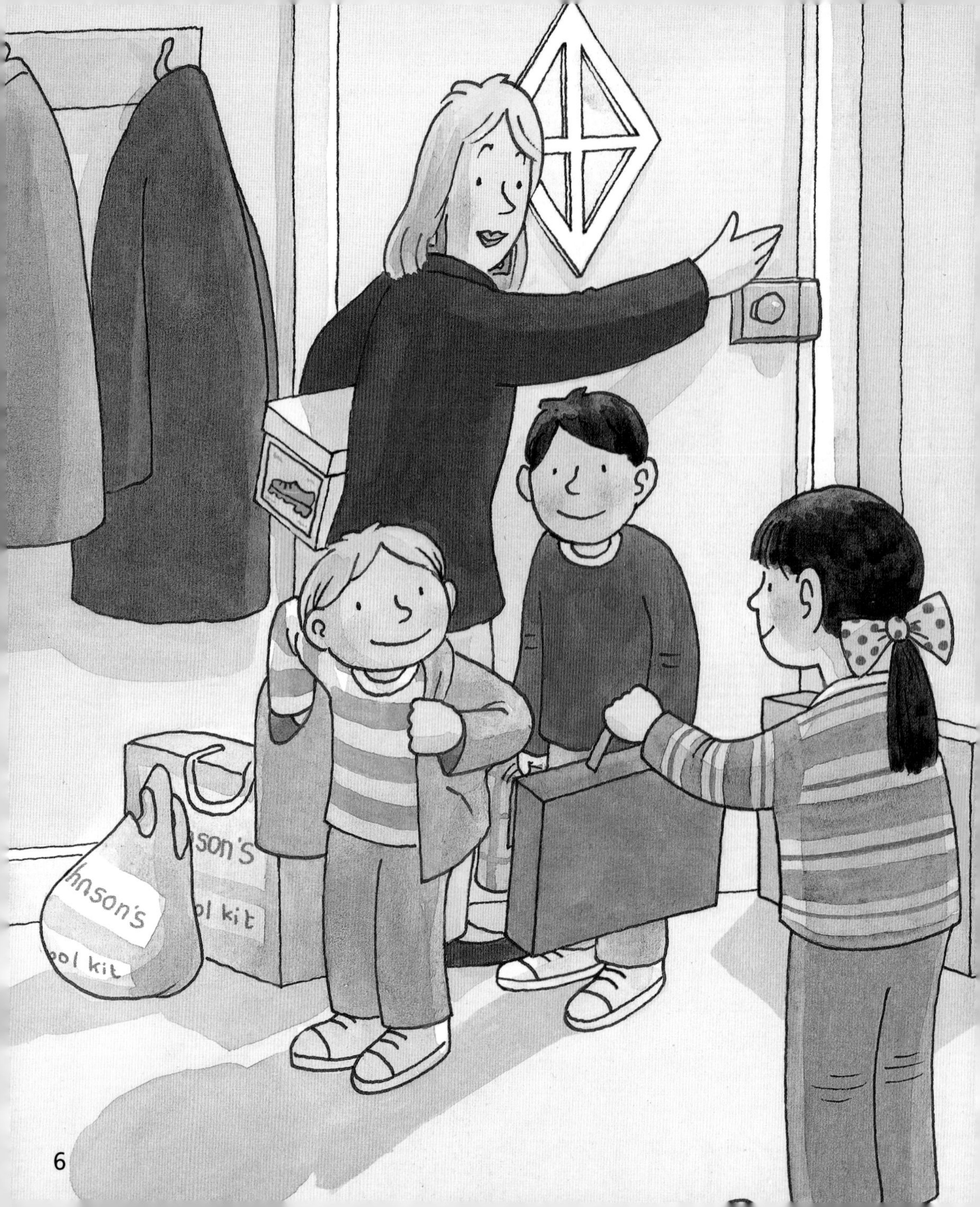
hnson's
ol kit
son's
ol kit

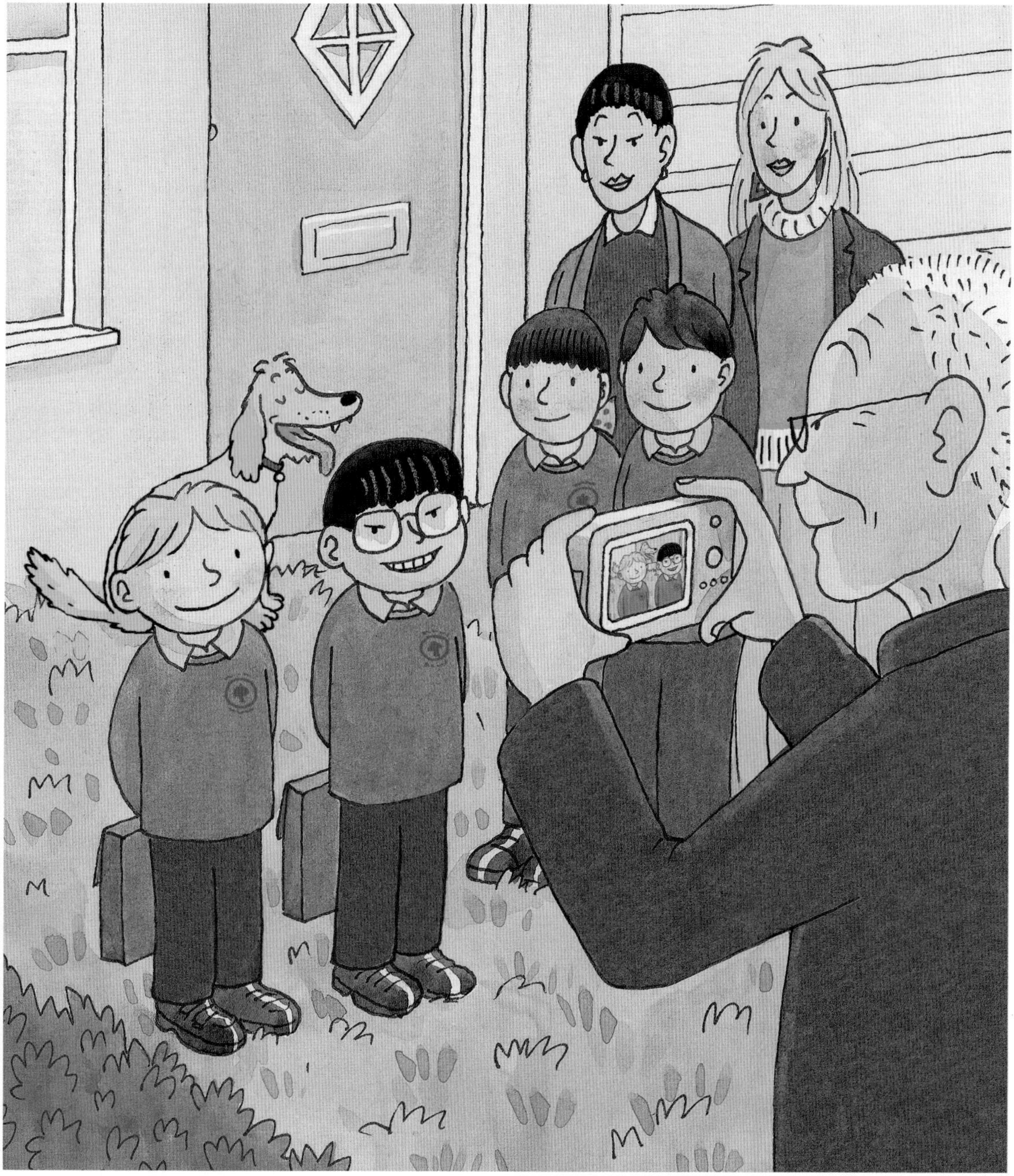

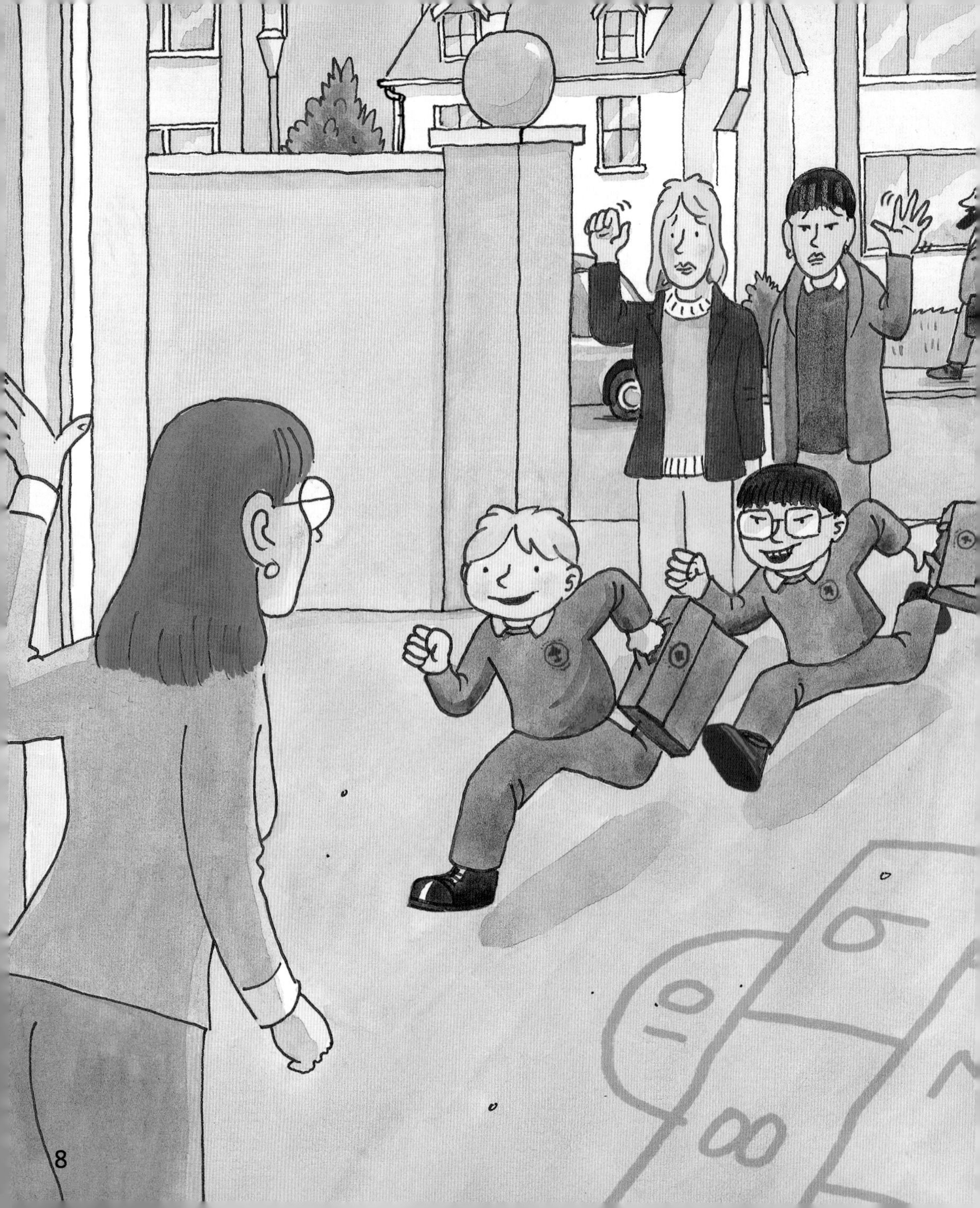